CGP has Phonics for Little Wandle sounded out!

CGP's Workbooks for Little Wandle are full of fun and friendly activities to build Year 1 pupils' confidence as they learn to read and write.

They follow the Little Wandle Letters and Sounds Revised programme exactly, so you can be sure they cover everything children need.

This is the **Year 1 Workbook** for **Autumn Term**.
It contains a recap of **Phases 3** and **4** of the Little Wandle Programme and the first part of **Phase 5**, including:

- Alternative spellings of vowel sounds
- Split digraphs
- Tricky words

What CGP is all about

Our sole aim here at CGP is to produce the highest quality books — carefully written, immaculately presented and dangerously close to being funny.

Then we work our socks off to get them out to you — at the cheapest possible prices.

Contents

Editors: Claire Boulter, Helen Clements, Catherine Heygate, Kirsty Sweetman
Contributor: Juliette Green
With thanks to Emma Crighton, Juliette Green and Marta Lukanowska for the proofreading.
With thanks to Alice Dent for the copyright research.

"Little Wandle" is a registered trade mark of the Wandle Learning Trust. Please note that CGP is not associated with Little Wandle or the Wandle Learning Trust in any way. This book does not include any official questions and is not endorsed by Wandle Learning Trust.

ISBN: 978 1 83774 160 1
Images on the cover and throughout © Educlips 2024
Printed by Elanders Ltd, Newcastle upon Tyne.
Based on the classic CGP style created by Richard Parsons.

How to Use this Book

This book is for children to complete in the <u>Autumn Term</u> of <u>Year 1</u>. It matches the <u>Little Wandle</u> phonics scheme.

The box at the top of the page contains <u>instructions</u>. Read through these with your child and go through the <u>worked example</u> so they know what to do.

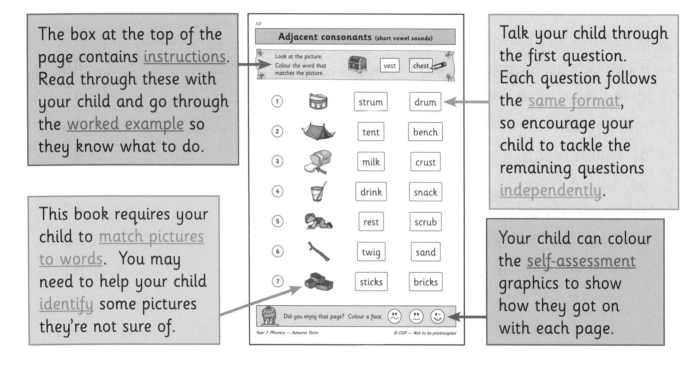

Talk your child through the first question. Each question follows the <u>same format</u>, so encourage your child to tackle the remaining questions <u>independently</u>.

This book requires your child to <u>match pictures to words</u>. You may need to help your child <u>identify</u> some pictures they're not sure of.

Your child can colour the <u>self-assessment</u> graphics to show how they got on with each page.

Phonics Hints for Helpers

- <u>Pronunciation</u> of some words will vary between different <u>accents</u>. If a child's accent doesn't follow the pronunciation suggested in this book they should practice reading the words in <u>their own accent</u>.

- A <u>grapheme</u> is a letter or group of letters that represents one sound.

- A <u>digraph</u> is a grapheme which uses two letters to represent one sound.

- A <u>trigraph</u> is a grapheme which uses three letters to represent one sound.

- A <u>split vowel digraph</u> is a digraph where the two letters of the grapheme are <u>separated</u> in a word. A <u>curved line</u> is used as a reminder that these letters are working together to make one sound.

| h | o | p | e |

- <u>Word frames</u> are used in spelling activities. There is usually one box for each <u>grapheme</u> (split vowel digraphs have two). Digraphs and trigraphs have wider boxes than single-letter graphemes.

| sh | a | p | e |

- <u>Tricky words</u> are common words which contain a sound that has not been learned yet. In some tricky words, the letters make a sound that does not correspond to the pronunciation children might expect.

| oh | Mr |
| our | |

Scan the QR code for more information about phonics. You can also find this information at: cgpbooks.co.uk/rocket

Phonics Guide

ai, ee, igh

Look at the picture.
Colour the word that
matches the picture.

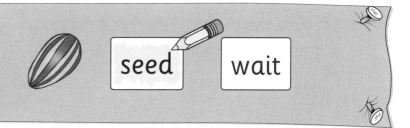

seed | wait

 **1** | see | rain

 6 | feed | bee

 2 | rail | light

 7 | sail | deep

 **3** | weep | sigh

 8 | right | high

 4 | nail | tight

 9 | feet | tail

 5 | hail | night

 10 | fight | peel

How do you feel about ai, ee and igh?

Year 1 Phonics — Autumn Term

oa, oo, ar

Look at the picture. Add the missing digraph to complete the word.

Choose from these digraphs:

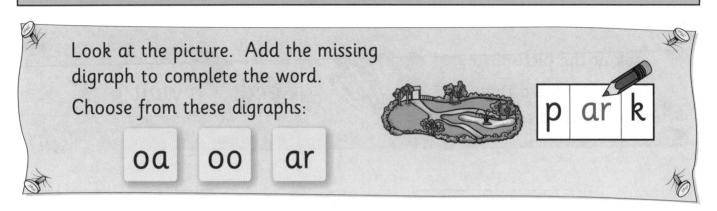

| oa | oo | ar |

| p | ar | k |

1 | p | | l |

5 | l | | f |

2 | c | | d |

6 | m | | n |

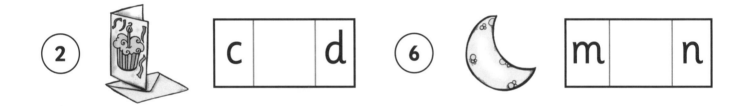

3 | r | | d |

7 | h | | p |

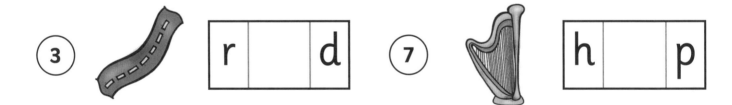

4 | b | | t |

8 | c | | t |

Do you feel confident about this page?

or, ur, oo

Look at the picture.
Circle the caption that
matches the picture.
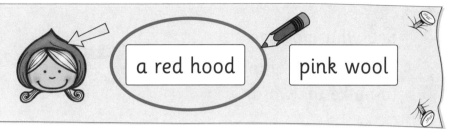
(a red hood)   pink wool

1 | his foot | his curl |

2  | they surf | they sort |

3  | a cork | a fork |

4 | burn the wood | turn a car |

5 | it is a hook | it is a horn |

6  | some fur | some corn |

7 | look at a book | be a cook |

 How did you get on with or, ur and oo?

Year 1 Phonics — Autumn Term

ow, oi, ear

Say what you see.
Then use the graphemes to make the word.

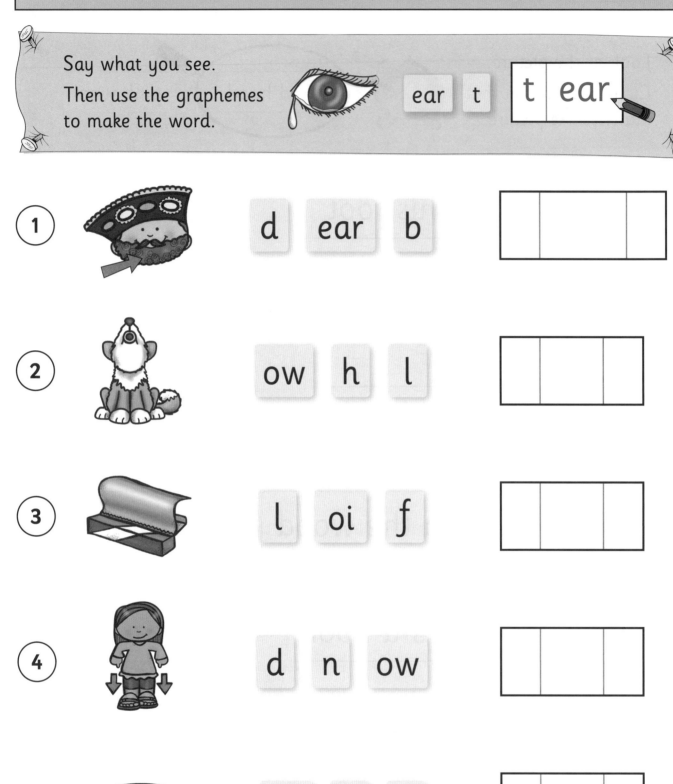

| ear | t | | t | ear |

1. d | ear | b

2. ow | h | l

3. l | oi | f

4. d | n | ow

5. oi | n | c

How did you find completing this page?

Mixed practice

Read each sentence. Then draw a line to match it to the correct picture.

It was her turn to wait with my goat.

1 I am joining him by his boat.

2 We might go into the shop to get a gown.

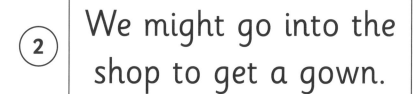 

3 Can you hear the owl out in the wood?

4 There were no sheep on the farm.

5 It was too dark for them to see so they took a light.

 How did this mixed practice go?

Year 1 Phonics — Autumn Term

er, air

Say the sound.
Circle the picture that contains this sound.

er

(1) er

(2) air

(3) er

(4) air

(5) er

(6) air

(7) er

 How well do you think this page went?

Words with s and es

Look at the picture.
Colour the caption that matches the picture.

| dog runs |
| cat naps |

1

| feeds me | hugs me |

2

| they like farms | we love parks |

3

| the dishes | his boxes |

4

| goats have horns | foxes have tails |

5

| loves books | sings songs |

6

| dad cooks | he visits nan |

 How did you get on with this page?

　　　　　　Year 1 Phonics — Autumn Term

Words with two or more digraphs

Say what you see.
Then use the graphemes to make the word.

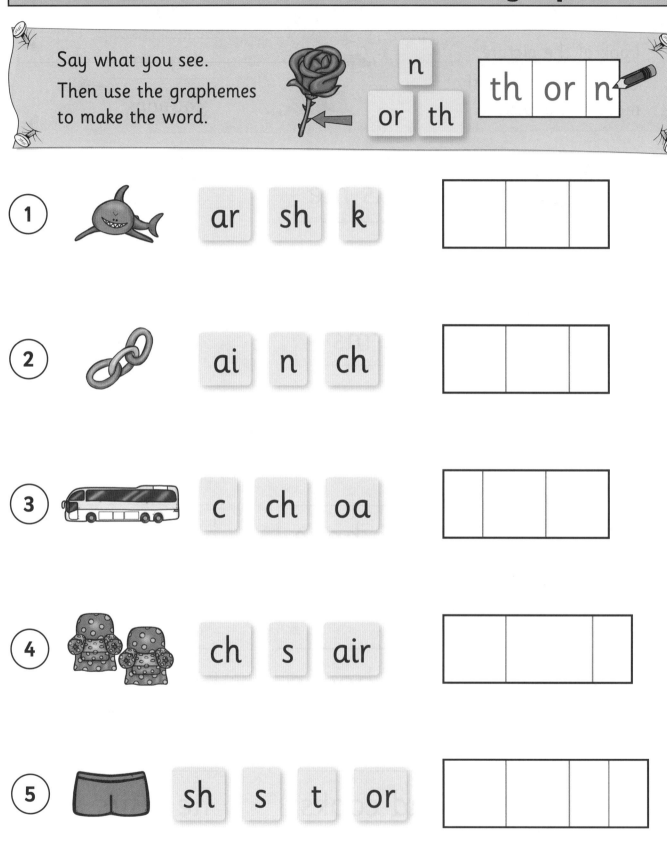

| th | or | n |

1. | ar | sh | k |

2. | ai | n | ch |

3. | c | ch | oa |

4. | ch | s | air |

5. | sh | s | t | or |

 How did you find the words on this page?

Words with two or more digraphs

Read the word.
Circle the picture that matches the word.

march

① tooth

② queen

③ sheep

④ torch

⑤ shopper

⑥ thigh

⑦ shower

 Colour a face to show how you did.

Year 1 Phonics — Autumn Term

Adjacent consonants (short vowel sounds)

Look at the picture.
Colour the word that
matches the picture.

  vest   chest

(1)   strum   drum

(2)    tent   bench

(3)    milk   crust

(4)   drink   snack

(5)    rest   scrub

(6)   twig   sand

(7)    sticks   bricks

  Did you enjoy that page? Colour a face.

Adjacent consonants (short vowel sounds)

Say what you see.
Then write the
word in the frame.

f | i | l | m

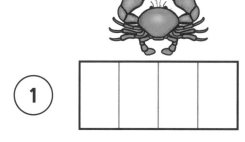

1

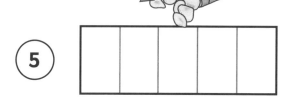

5

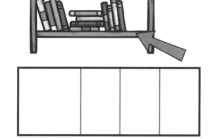

2

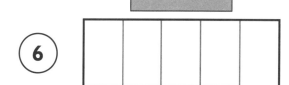

6

3

7

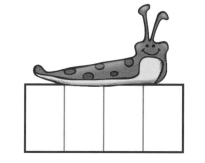

4

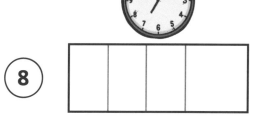

8

How do you feel after finishing this page?

Year 1 Phonics — Autumn Term

Adjacent consonants (long vowel sounds)

 Read the word.
Then write a rhyming word in the frame.
The pictures will help.  scar

1 coast

2 groom

3 street

4 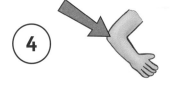 joint

5 stain

6 brown

 Do you feel good about this page?

Adjacent consonants (long vowel sounds)

Read each sentence. Then draw a line to match it to the best picture.

They were looking at
the lightning storm.

(1) The artist was
painting some flowers.

(2) Come downstairs
so I can hear you.

(3) Abbas felt glad as he
slurped his hot drink.

(4) She pointed at the
bright stars up there.

(5) His fortress was at the
top of a steep hill.

Colour a face to show how that went.

Year 1 Phonics — Autumn Term

'ai' sound spelt ay

Look at the picture.
Circle the caption that
matches the picture.

(in the day)   at night

1

a play   a book

2

a brown cat   a stray dog

3

clay in
his hand   paint in
her hair

4

on a tray   on a spoon

5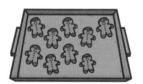

he is
singing   he is
swaying

6

black crayon   green pen

 How did you find the 'ai' sound spelt ay?

'ow' sound spelt ou

Read the sentence.
Then write it on
the dotted line.

There were lots of clouds.

There were lots of clouds.

(1) Do you like to shout?

......

(2) We push the box around.

......

(3) She sat on the ground.

......

(4) He found some insects.

......

 How do you feel about this page?

Year 1 Phonics — Autumn Term

'oi' sound spelt oy

Read the word.
Colour the picture that matches the word.

boys

(1) toy

(2) spray

(3) joy

(4) tray

(5) stay

(6) destroy

(7) oyster

(8) praying

 How do you think this page went?

'ee' sound spelt ea

Look at the picture.
Write the missing word
to complete the caption.
Each word has this digraph: ea

| ea | t | with a spoon |

1  have a | | | |

2  a soft | | | |

3  play on the | | | |

4 eggs on a | | | |

5  | | | the drum

6 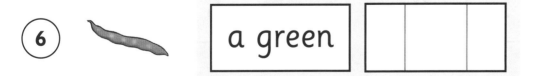 a green | | | |

 How did you find this page?

Year 1 Phonics — Autumn Term

Mixed practice

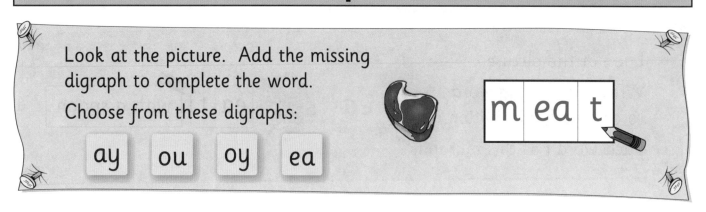

Look at the picture. Add the missing digraph to complete the word.

Choose from these digraphs:

ay **ou** **oy** **ea**

m | ea | t

1. s | p | r | | t

5. t | r | | t | s

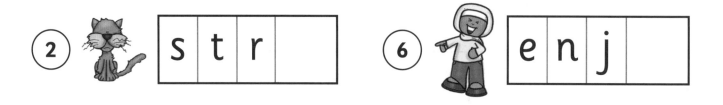

2. | s | t | r |

6. e | n | j |

3. r | | d | i | ng

7. s | | n | d

4. | s | t | er

8. s | | i | ng

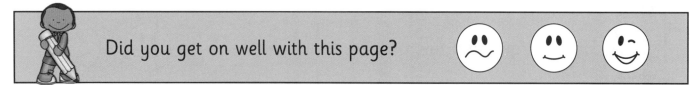

Did you get on well with this page?

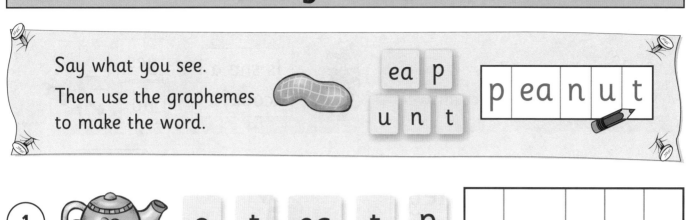

Longer words

Say what you see.
Then use the graphemes to make the word.

ea p
u nt

p	e	a	n	u	t

1 | o | t | ea | t | p |

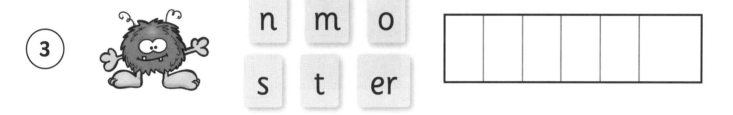

2 | m | ear | u | s | ff |

3 | n | m | o | s | t | er |

4 | air | c | h | u | t |

5 | p | p | c | or | n | o |

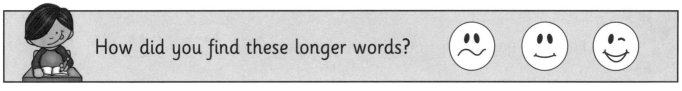

How did you find these longer words?

Half-term recap

Read the question.
Then tick the correct answer.

 Is she a cook?

 yes ☐
 no ✔

1 What are they feeling today?

joy ☐
pain ☐

2 What did Arthur do?

clean up ☐
cook food ☐

3 When will I sail my boat?

at night ☐
in the day ☐

4 What was the king counting?

his letters ☐
some coins ☐

5 Is Burt playing a sport?

yes he is ☐
no he is not ☐

 How do you think you did on this page?

Half-term recap

 Read the sentence. Then write it on the dotted line.

I am here in the tower.

I am here in the tower.

(1) He feeds all the ducklings.

....

(2) She waited near the airport.

....

(3) One boy plays the harp.

....

(4) I found a crab by the sea.

....

 How did that go? Colour a face.

'ur' sound spelt ir

Look at the picture.
Colour the caption that matches the picture. | a sad boy | a glad girl

1 | a skirt | a shirt

2  | first on the moon | third in the room

3 | stack of books | heap of dirt

4  | twirling | crouching

5 | brown bird | red rabbit

6  | you play the drums | he stirs the batter

 Colour a face to show how that went.

Year 1 Phonics — Autumn Term

'igh' sound spelt ie

Say what you see.
Then use the graphemes to make the word.

| ie | p |

| p | ie |

1  ie s t

2  r ie f d

3   d r c ie

4  p s ie s

5   l s f ie

 How did you get on with that page?

Year 1 Phonics — Autumn Term

'oo' and 'yoo' sounds spelt ue

Read the word.
Circle the picture that matches the word.

cue

① glue

② blue

③ rescue

④ clue

⑤ argue

⑥ true

 Do you feel good about this page?

'yoo' sound spelt u

 Read the caption.
Then colour the picture that matches the caption.

a human

1 tin of tuna

2 look at a menu

3 boy in uniform

4 a unicorn horn

5 enjoy the music

6 lots of units

 Did this page go well? Colour a face.

Year 1 Phonics — Autumn Term

Tricky words

Trace the tricky words.
Then copy the right tricky word to complete each sentence.

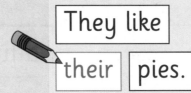

They like

their pies.

| their | people | oh | your |

(1) You have a stain on

[   ] blue shirt.

Don't forget to use a capital letter at the start of a sentence.

(2) The [   ] jig to music.

(3) They brush [   ] teeth.

(4) [   ] no, you fell in the dirt!

(5) Lots of [   ] sit.

How did you find those tricky words?

Mixed practice

Read each sentence. Then draw a line to match it to the correct picture.

The bird flies to a nest in the tree.

1. We looked for clues and found the footprints.

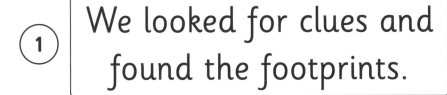

2. He cried when the unicorn left.

3. They argued about what music to play first.

4. The girl in uniform stirs the pot of hot food.

5. The maths teacher has a blue tie and a smart shirt.

 Colour a face to show how you did.

Year 1 Phonics — Autumn Term

'oa' sound spelt o

Read the words.
Colour the word where the
grapheme **o** makes the '**oa**' sound.

 gold

 fox

clock

1 cold | rocket | blob

2 stop | cobweb | hello

3 strong | post | golf

4 holiday | shock | open

5 folder | robin | pocket

 Do you feel okay about the 'oa' sound?

'igh' sound spelt i

Read the words.
Draw a line to match each word to the best picture.

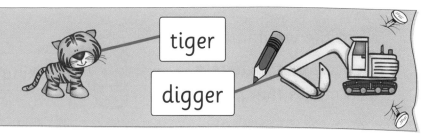

tiger

digger

1

child

traffic

2

spinning

spider

3

twins

driver

4

singer

rider

How did you find this page?

Year 1 Phonics — Autumn Term

'ai' sound spelt a

Read the word in the box.
Tick the word where **a**
also makes the '**ai**' sound.

baking

| grating | ✔ |
| mashing | ☐ |

---

① waving

shaking ☐

clapping ☐

---

②  skating

spanner ☐

apricot ☐

---

③  raking

rabbit ☐

paper ☐

---

④  tasting

carrot ☐

acorn ☐

 What did you make of this page?

'ee' sound spelt e

Read the caption.
Circle the picture that
best matches the caption.

a refund
for me

1 he can see me

2 being good

3 keep a secret

4 run a relay

5 in bed with
a fever

 Colour a face to show how that went.

Year 1 Phonics — Autumn Term

Tricky words

 Read the sentence. Then write it on the dotted line.

Mrs David had a cold.

 Mrs David had a cold.

(1) | Ms Peters is so kind. |

(2) | He is waving to Mrs Chen. |

(3) | Mr Davis is holding folders. |

(4) | I ask for some paper. |

In some accents, the word **ask** isn't tricky.

 Have you mastered these tricky words?

Mixed practice

Colour in the word that completes the sentence so that it matches the picture.

The | child | mild | is skating.

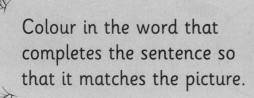

1  He is | making / chasing | his bed.

2  The | spider / tiger | is smiling.

3  Zainab will | most / post | a letter.

4  We told Ms Green a | secret. / fever.

 How are these sounds shaping up?

'ai' sound spelt a-e

Read the word.
Circle the picture that matches the word.

ape

(1) wave

(2) spade

(3) grapes

(4) skate

(5) plate

(6) flame

(7) pancake

 How would you rate this page?

'igh' sound spelt i-e

 Look at the picture.
Colour the word that
matches the picture.

 | prize | pride |

1  | five | dive |

2 | time | line |

3 | ripe | pipe |

4 | slime | slide |

5 | drive | stride |

6  | outside | inside |

7  | beehive | sunshine |

 Did you shine on this page?

Year 1 Phonics — Autumn Term

'oa' sound spelt o-e

Look at the picture.
Add the missing digraph to complete the word.

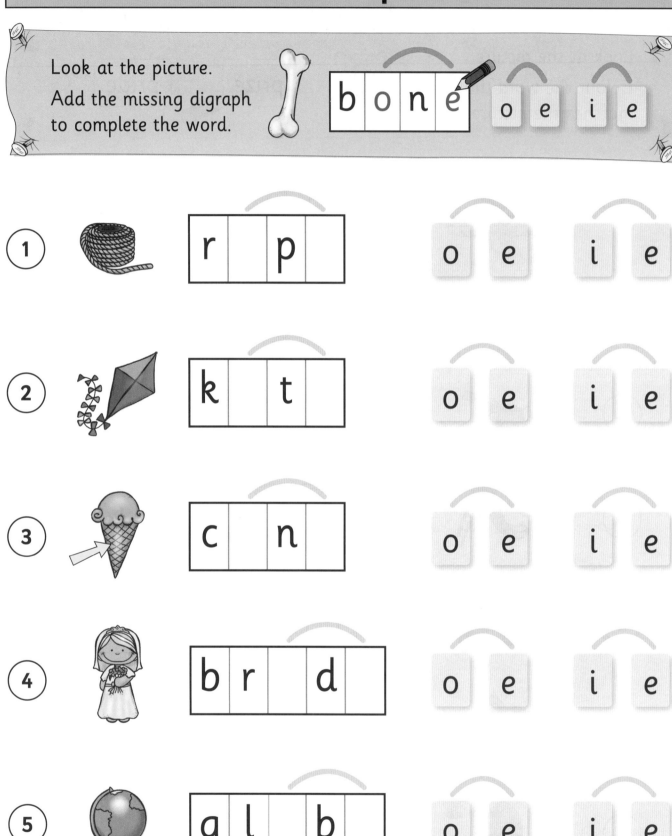

| b | o | n | e |

o e   i e

1   r _ p   o e   i e

2   k _ t   o e   i e

3   c _ n   o e   i e

4   b r _ d   o e   i e

5   g l _ b   o e   i e

 Did you feel at home with those words?

'oo' and 'yoo' sounds spelt u-e

Look at the picture.
Circle the caption that matches the picture.

a peach   (a prune)

1) | a blue cone | a red cube |

2)  | a tune on the flute | a tune on the harp |

3)  | a costume | a skirt |

4)  | bar of soap | tube of paint |

5) | sand dune | dark cave |

6) | a cute rabbit | a cute mule |

 Did you get on well with this page?

Year 1 Phonics — Autumn Term

Tricky words

Read the sentence.
Then write it on
the dotted line.

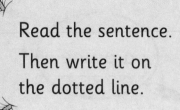

I drove our car.

I drove our car.

1 Luke could use a broom.

2 I would like to have a snake.

3 I should get a notebook.

4 The waiter took our order.

 How would you say you did this time?

Mixed practice

Read the question.
Then tick the correct answer.

| Is the perfume green? | yes ☐ |
| | no ☑ |

1 What has Nella got on her back?

a cape ☐

a robe ☐

2 Are there five roses?

yes there are ☐

no there are not ☐

3 Is Clive on his bike outside?

he is ☐

he is not ☐

4 What is on my plate?

a lime ☐

some cake ☐

5 What will June do today?

bake a pie ☐

use a hose ☐

 Was this page a piece of cake?

Year 1 Phonics — Autumn Term

'ee' sound spelt e-e

Read the words.
Circle the picture that
matches each word or phrase.

compete

1 athlete

2 even

3 concrete

4 theme park

5 evening

6 complete

 Did this page go extremely well?

'oo' and 'yoo' sounds spelt ew

Say what you see.
Then use the graphemes to make the word.

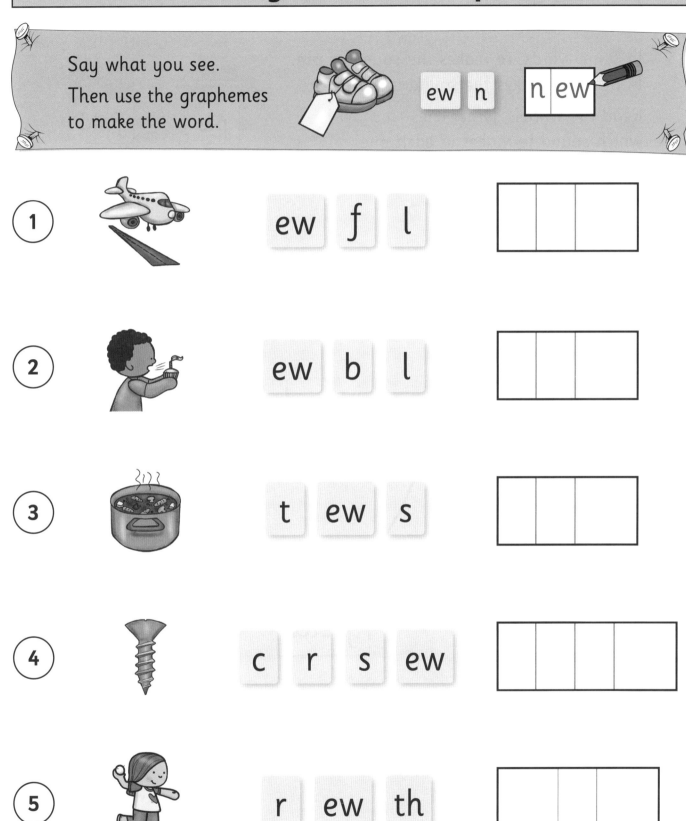

1. ew f l

2. ew b l

3. t ew s

4. c r s ew

5. r ew th

 Did you get a few right? Colour a face.

'ee' sound spelt ie

In some words, **ie** makes the sound in **pie**.
In others it makes the sound in **field**.

Read the words. Draw lines to show
which sound **ie** makes in each one.

pie

field

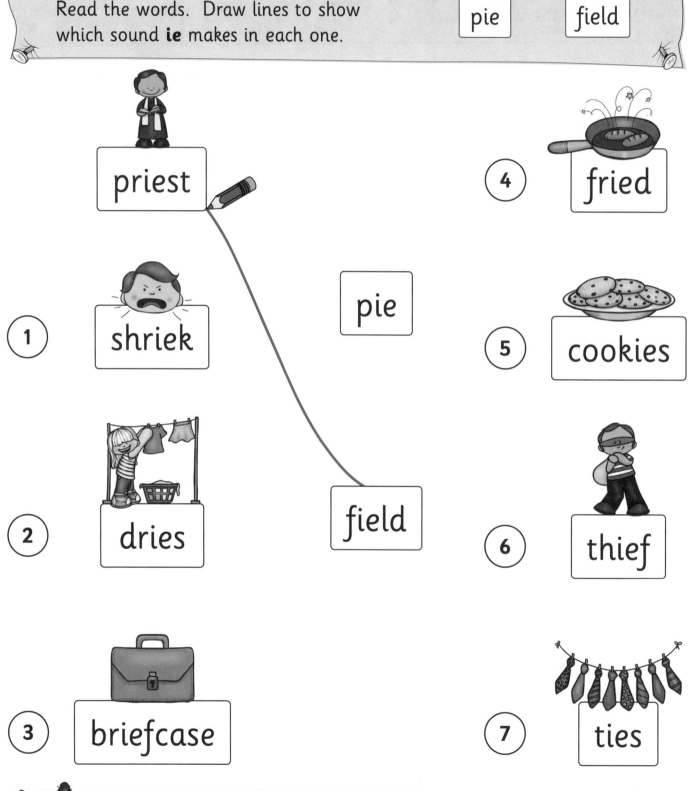

priest

(1) shriek

(2) dries

(3) briefcase

(4) fried

pie

(5) cookies

field

(6) thief

(7) ties

 Have you achieved a lot on this page?

'or' sound spelt aw

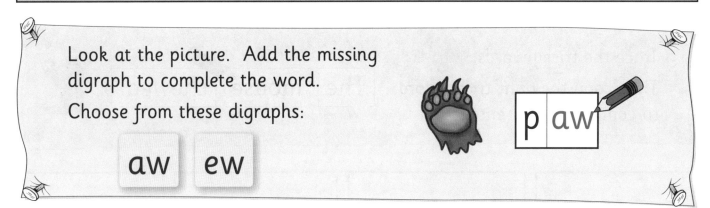

Look at the picture. Add the missing digraph to complete the word.

Choose from these digraphs:

aw ew

| p | aw |

 1 | y | | n |

 5 | l | | n |

 2 | g | r | |

 6 | n | | s |

 3 | ch | |

 7 | c | r | l |

 4 | c | l | |

 8 | s | t | r | |

 Are you awesome at these sounds?

Tricky words

Trace the tricky words.
Then copy the right tricky word to complete each sentence.

The | mouse | chewed.

| house | mouse | water | want |

1 I ☐ a shawl like Annie.

2 These flowers need ☐ .

3 Andrew has a pet ☐ .

4 My ☐ is in a field.

5 I ☐ to help

Billie complete her jigsaw.

 How did you find those tricky words?

Mixed practice

Read each sentence. Then draw a line to match it to the correct picture.

I saw Shawn holding a shield.

1 Three blue birds squawked and shrieked.

2 We flew round the theme park ride.

3 The seesaw in the park is not quite even.

4 Lizzie drew her new house on paper.

5 Eve has fewer pens than Lewis so he lends her one.

Colour a face to show how you did.

Year 1 Phonics — Autumn Term

'igh' sound recap

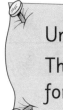

Underline the '**igh**' sound in each word.
Then write out all the different graphemes for the '**igh**' sound that you have found.

li<u>me</u>   t<u>ie</u>

① frighten

② time

③ pie

④ wild

⑤ cries

⑥ flight

⑦ find

⑧ bike

⑨ lightning

⑩ smile

⑪ ☐ ☐☐ ☐ ☐

How did you like this page?

'ai' sound recap

Read each word.
Then write each one under the grapheme that it contains.

rain

ai

rain

(1) spray

(5) paper

(2) crayon

(6) skate

(3) train

(7) acorn

(4) blaze

(8) paint

ay   ai   a   a e

 Did you sail through this page?

Year 1 Phonics — Autumn Term

'oa' sound recap

Read the word.
Then write a rhyming word in the frame.
The pictures will help.

 robe   g l o b e

1 toad

2 gold

3 throat

4  no

5 rose

6 bone

 How did this page go?

'ee' sound recap

Read the sentence.
Underline all the graphemes that make the '**ee**' sound.

W<u>e</u> can <u>ea</u>t th<u>e</u>se sw<u>ee</u>ts.

① The sheep are in a field.

② We screamed at the theme park.

③ Pete the priest felt full of glee.

④ These athletes compete.

⑤ She is the cookie thief.

⑥ I see a steaming pan of peas.

⑦ My top has a green leaf on it.

 Are you feeling pleased about this page?

'oo' and 'yoo' sounds recap

Read each word.
Tick the word that contains the
same sound as the grapheme in red.

blue

pool ✔

boat ☐

1. newspaper

drum ☐

rescue ☐

2. flute

moon ☐

storm ☐

3. unicorn

perfume ☐

surf ☐

4. glue

duck ☐

chew ☐

Is it true that you did well on this page?

Autumn term recap

Read each sentence. Then draw a line to match it to the correct picture.

Rose puts your straw in the water.

1. Eve is baking in her blue hat.

2. The cute newts enjoy crawling on the beach.

3. The robot smiles when people play music.

4. The child wants a bite of their pie.

5. The bird flew right over the clouds.

 Are you smiling after this page?

Year 1 Phonics — Autumn Term

Autumn term recap

 Read the sentence.
Then write it on
the dotted line.

The mouse holds a leaf.

.The mouse holds a leaf..

1 You should stay at our house.

2 I asked if I could use his bike.

3 Mr Jones hates spiders.

4 They argue in a field.

 How did you get on with this recap?

Year 1 Phonics — Autumn Term